Going to Hospital

Written by Sandra Iversen • Illustrated by Rick Youmans

David fell out of the tree.
He hurt his leg.
"Don't be afraid," said Dad.
"I will call the ambulance.
It will take you to the hospital."

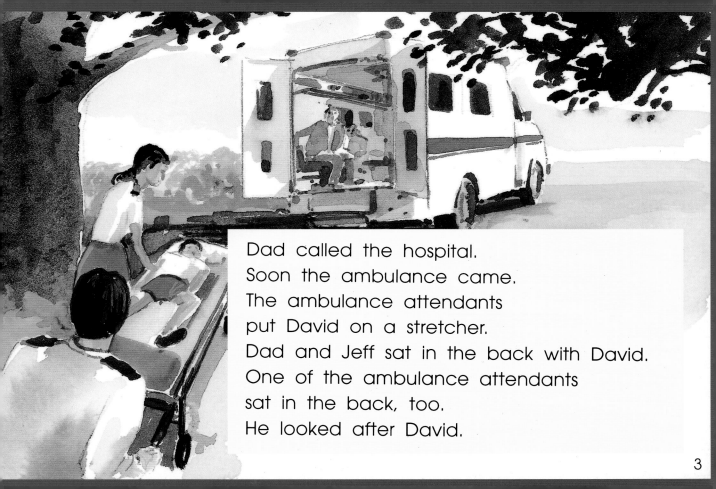

Dad called the hospital.
Soon the ambulance came.
The ambulance attendants
put David on a stretcher.
Dad and Jeff sat in the back with David.
One of the ambulance attendants
sat in the back, too.
He looked after David.

3

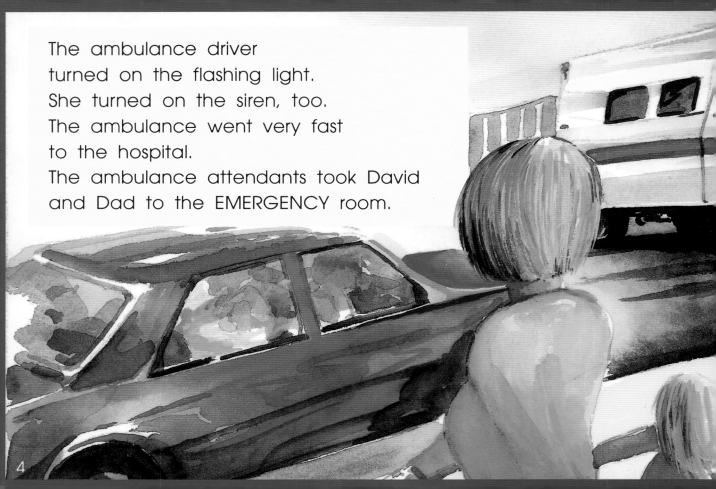

The ambulance driver
turned on the flashing light.
She turned on the siren, too.
The ambulance went very fast
to the hospital.
The ambulance attendants took David
and Dad to the EMERGENCY room.

4

HOSPITAL→

5

Dad filled out a form.
He wrote David's name.
He wrote David's address.
He wrote David's age.
He told the nurse that
David fell out of the tree
and hurt his leg.

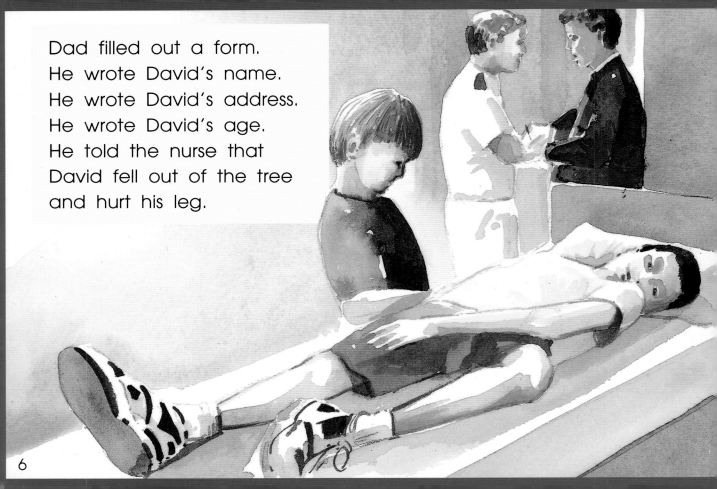

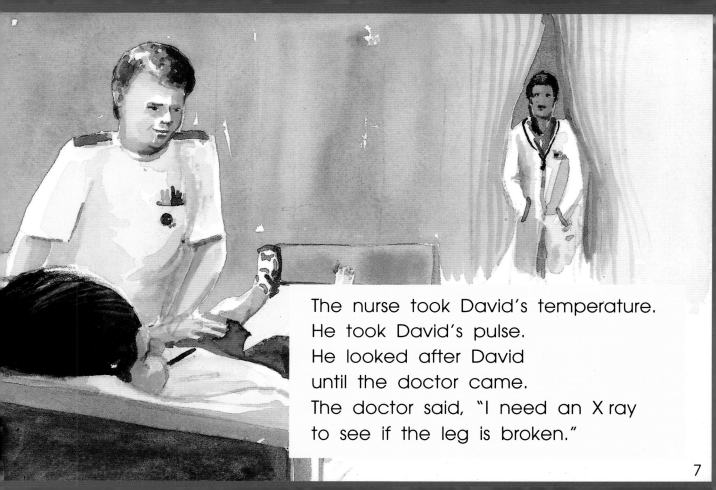

The nurse took David's temperature.
He took David's pulse.
He looked after David
until the doctor came.
The doctor said, "I need an X ray
to see if the leg is broken."

The nurse took David to X RAY.
The X ray nurse had a big camera.
She told David to lie very still.
She took a picture of David's leg.
"I will send the picture to the doctor," she said.
"She will see if your leg is broken."

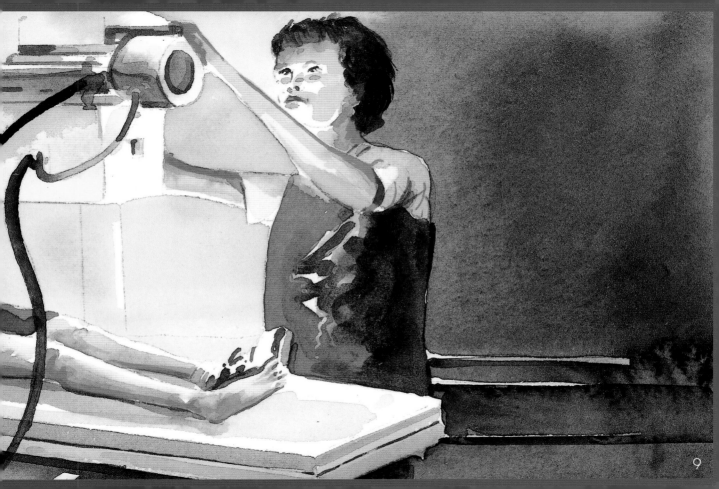

The nurse took David back to
the EMERGENCY room.
The doctor looked at the picture of David's leg.
"It's broken here," she said.

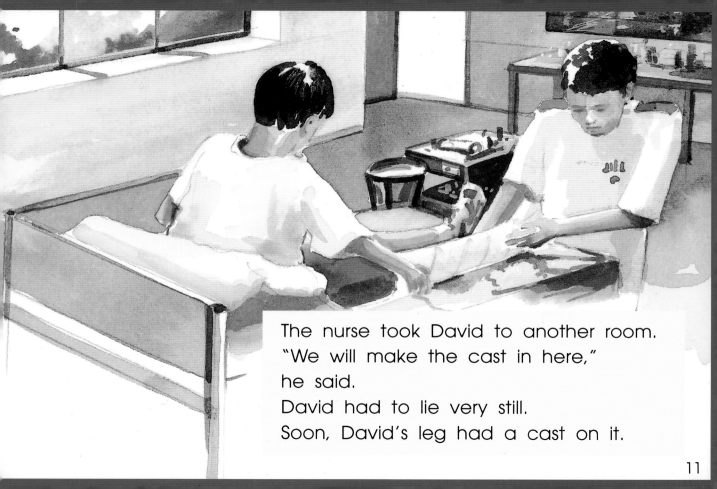

The nurse took David to another room.
"We will make the cast in here,"
he said.
David had to lie very still.
Soon, David's leg had a cast on it.

"You can take David home now,"
the nurse said to Dad.
"He must not walk on his leg.
He must not get his leg wet."

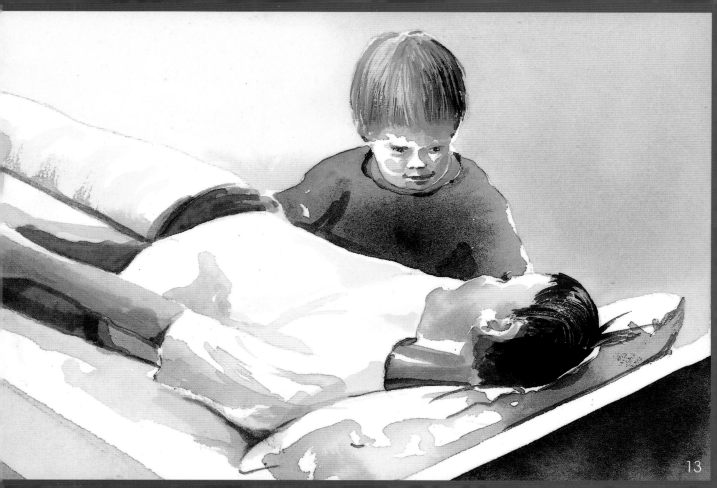

"You must come back to the hospital
next week.
We will check your cast for you.
Soon your leg will be mended."

The nurse lifted David into a wheelchair
and took him to the door.
Dad called a taxi.
He lifted David in.
David and Dad and Jeff went home.